rockschool®

Female Vocals
Grade 7

Performance pieces, technical exercises and in-depth guidance
for Rockschool examinations

Acknowledgements

Published by Rockschool Ltd. © 2014 under license from Music Sales Ltd.
Catalogue Number RSK091407
ISBN: 978-1-908920-57-7

AUDIO
Backing tracks produced by Music Sales Limited
Supporting test backing tracks recorded by Jon Musgrave, Jon Bishop and Duncan Jordan
Supporting test vocals recorded by Duncan Jordan
Supporting tests mixed at Langlei Studios by Duncan Jordan
Mastered by Duncan Jordan

MUSICIANS
Neal Andrews, Lucie Burns (Lazy Hammock), Jodie Davies,Tenisha Edwards, Noam Lederman,
Beth Loates-Taylor, Dave Marks, Salena Mastroianni, Paul Miro, Ryan Moore, Jon Musgrave,
Chris Smart, Ross Stanley, T-Jay, Stacy Taylor, Daniel Walker

PUBLISHING
Compiled and edited by James Uings, Simon Troup, Stephen Lawson and Stuart Slater
Internal design and layout by Simon and Jennie Troup, Digital Music Art
Cover designed by Philip Millard, Philip Millard Design
Fact Files written by Stephen Lawson, Owen Bailey and Michael Leonard
Additional proofing by Chris Bird, Ronan Macdonald, Jonathan Preiss and Becky Baldwin
Cover photography © Brian Rasic / Rex Features
Full transcriptions by Music Sales Ltd.

SYLLABUS
Vocal specialists: Martin Hibbert and Eva Brandt
Additional Consultation: Emily Nash, Stuart Slater and Sarah Page
Supporting Tests Composition: Martin Hibbert, James Uings, Jon Musgrave, Jodie Davies,
Ryan Moore, Chris Hawkins, Jonathan Preiss

PRINTING
Printed and bound in the United Kingdom by Caligraving Ltd.
Media hosting by Dropcards

DISTRIBUTION
Exclusive Distributors: Music Sales Ltd.

CONTACTING ROCKSCHOOL
www.rockschool.co.uk
Telephone: +44 (0)845 460 4747
Fax: +44 (0)845 460 1960

Table of Contents

Welcome to Rockschool Female Vocals Grade 7

Welcome to the Rockschool Female Vocals Grade 7 pack. This book and accompanying download card contain everything you need to sing at this grade.

Vocals Exams

At each grade you have the option of taking one of two different types of examination:

- **Grade Exam:** a Grade Exam is a mixture of music performances, technical work and tests. You prepare three pieces (two of which may be Free Choice Pieces) and the contents of the Technical Exercise section. This accounts for 75% of the exam marks. The other 25% consists of: a Quick Study Piece (10%), two Ear Tests (10%), and finally you will be asked five General Musicianship Questions (5%). The pass mark is 60%.

- **Performance Certificate:** in a Performance Certificate you sing five pieces. Up to three of these can be Free Choice Pieces. Each song is marked out of 20 and the pass mark is 60%.

Book Contents

The book is divided into a number of sections. These are:

- **Exam Pieces:** in this book you will find six well-known pieces of Grade 7 standard. Each song is preceded by a Fact File detailing information about the original recording, the artist who sang on it and some recommended listening if you wish to research the artist further.

- **Piano and guitar notation:** every exam piece is printed with a piano part and guitar chords. Both are a representation of the overall band arrangement. These have been included to assist you with your practice should you wish to use a piano and/or guitar for accompaniment. In your exam you must perform to the backing tracks provided.

- **Vocal score:** in addition to the piano/vocal/guitar arrangement there is also a separate vocal-only score to allow you to view the vocal part on a single sheet of paper.

- **Technical Exercises:** there are a range of technical exercises in this grade. Some are notated in full, and some give a range of starting notes.

- **Supporting Tests and General Musicianship Questions:** in Vocals Grade 7 there are three supporting tests – a Quick Study Piece, two Ear Tests and a set of General Musicianship Questions (GMQs) asked at the end of each exam. Examples of the types of tests likely to appear in the exam are printed in this book.

- **General Information:** finally, you will find information on exam procedures, including online examination entry, marking schemes, information on Free Choice Pieces and improvisation requirements for each grade.

Audio

Each song in Vocals Grade 7 has an audio track that can be downloaded via the download card that comes with the book. This is a backing track with the vocal taken off so you can sing along with the band. The backing tracks should be used in examinations. There are also audio examples of the supporting tests printed in the book.

The audio files are supplied in MP3 format, the most widely compatible audio format in common usage – MP3s will likely be familiar to anyone with a computer, iPod, smartphone or similar device. Once downloaded you will be able to play them on any compatible device; we hope that you find this extra versatility useful.

Download cards

Download cards are easy to use – simply go to *www.dropcards.com/rsvocals* and type in the code on the back of your card. It's best to do this somewhere with a good connection, to ensure that the download is uninterrupted. If you have any problems with your download, you should be able to resolve them at *www.dropcards.com/help*.

We hope you enjoy using this book. You can find further details about Rockschool's Vocals and other instrumental syllabuses on our website: *www.rockschool.co.uk*.

SONG TITLE: BIG SPENDER
ALBUM: AND WE WERE LOVERS
RELEASED: 1967
LABEL: UNITED ARTISTS
GENRE: SWING

PERSONNEL: SHIRLEY BASSEY (VOX)

UK CHART PEAK: 21
US CHART PEAK: N/A

BACKGROUND INFO

'Big Spender' was a hit single for Shirley Bassey in 1967 and featured on her album *And We Were Lovers*.

THE BIGGER PICTURE

Shirley Bassey was born in Cardiff, Wales in 1937. Bassey is known for her powerful vocals, which were first noticed (though not encouraged) by her school teachers: "Everyone told me to shut up!" she said. "Even in the school choir the teacher kept telling me to back off till I was singing in the corridor!" Bassey left school aged 14 and worked in a factory by day, while singing in pubs and clubs in the evenings. In 1953 and 1954, the teenaged Bassey appeared in a couple of travelling musical theatre productions. Later, during a performance in London's West End, she was spotted and offered a record deal. Her first single, 'Burn My Candle', was released in 1956. The following year she had her first hit with 'The Banana Boat Song', which went to Number 8 in the UK singles chart. Bassey's success peaked in the 1960s, during which her recording of the James Bond theme 'Goldfinger' gave the singer her only Top 40 hit in America, while climbing to Number 21 in the UK. In 1971, she was asked again to record a Bond theme for the film *Diamonds Are Forever*. (The track was later sampled by Kanye West on his song 'Diamonds From Sierra Leone'.) Bassey recorded her third James Bond theme, 'Moonraker', in 1979. She spent the 1980s in "semi-retirement", then received an unexpected boost of cool in 1997, when she featured on dance act the Propellerheads' single 'History Repeating'. In 1999, Queen Elizabeth II granted Bassey the title 'Dame' for her services to entertainment.

NOTES

'Big Spender' was written by Cy Coleman and Dorothy Fields for the Broadway musical *Sweet Charity*. The show was first performed in 1966 – a year before Shirley Bassey recorded her version of the song. Since it entered the Top 40 in 1967, 'Big Spender' has become a signature song for Bassey.

RECOMMENDED LISTENING

Shirley Bassey's James Bond songs are all essential. Her powerful vocals sit beautifully with the lush production typical of Bond themes. *Something* (1970) was a collection of rock and pop covers, and features a funky version of The Doors' 'Light My Fire' among other gems. The title track, a cover of The Beatles song, was a bigger hit in the UK than the original.

Big Spender

Shirley Bassey

Words by Dorothy Fields
Music by Cy Coleman

© Copyright 1965 by Cy Coleman.
Rights assigned to Notable Music Company, Inc. in co-publication with Lida Enterprises, Inc.
Administered by Chester Music Limited trading as Campbell Connelly & Co. for Australasia, the British Isles, Continental Europe, Eire, Israel, Japan and South Africa.
All Rights Reserved. International Copyright Secured.

SONG TITLE: BLEEDING LOVE
ALBUM: SPIRIT
RELEASED: 2007
LABEL: SYCO MUSIC
GENRE: R'N'B / POP

PERSONNEL: LEONA LEWIS (VOX)

UK CHART PEAK: 1
US CHART PEAK: 1

BACKGROUND INFO

'Bleeding Love' was the lead single from *The X Factor* winner Leona Lewis's debut album, *Spirit*.

THE BIGGER PICTURE

Leona Louise Lewis was born in London in 1985. When her parents realised she loved to sing, they sent her to the Sylvia Young and Italia Conti theatre schools, until they could no longer afford to. Her early influences were Minnie Ripperton, Eva Cassidy and Stevie Wonder. Later, she attended the BRIT School (other famous alumni include Jessie J, Adele and Amy Winehouse) but left so that she could get directly involved with the music scene. By then Lewis had started writing her own material, and she soon hooked up with a production company to record an album, which was used to try to get her a record deal. However, no offer was made. Another album was made with UEG Entertainment – again to no avail. Rather than give up, Lewis decided to audition for *The X Factor* in 2006. After favourable comparisons with Whitney Houston, Mariah Carey and Celine Dion, she won with 60 per cent of the public vote. Her prize was a £1 million recording contract with judge Simon Cowell's Syco Music. A contract in America with Clive Davis's J Records followed in 2007.

NOTES

'Bleeding Love' was written by OneRepublic frontman Ryan Tedder and singer-songwriter Jesse McCartney for the latter's studio album *Departure*. However, McCartney's record company turned the song down, claiming it wasn't strong enough for the album. Despite their disappointment, the pair decided to offer the song to Leona Lewis when they got word that the singer was looking for tracks for her debut album, *Spirit*. When Simon Cowell heard 'Bleeding Love', he told Ryan Tedder it was "the one". Tedder: "I said, I think she could kill this song. I rearranged it for her, changed the key, tailored it for her voice. She absolutely took control of it and owned it." In the end, McCartney got his wish, sort of – he recorded 'Bleeding Love' and it featured as a bonus track on the international version of his album.

RECOMMENDED LISTENING

'Better In Time', from the same album as 'Bleeding Love', is a more R'n'B-flavoured production and was another Top 10 hit for Lewis. While appearing as a guest on Radio 1's Jo Whiley Show, Lewis performed a powerful acoustic version of the Snow Patrol song 'Run'. She later recorded a studio version for the deluxe edition of *Spirit*.

Bleeding Love

Leona Lewis
Words & Music by Jesse McCartney & Ryan Tedder

© Copyright 2007 Artemis Muziekuitgeverij B.V/Write 2 Live Publishing.
Warner/Chappell Artemis Music Limited/Kobalt Music Publishing Limited.
All Rights Reserved. International Copyright Secured.

C Csus4 C Csus4 C Csus4 C Csus4
To Coda
You cut me o - pen,
F F Fsus2
ooh.
2.Try - ing hard not to hear but they talk so loud,
Dm7 Fsus2/D B♭maj9
their pierc - ing sounds fill my ears, try to fill me with doubt, yet I know that the
B♭6/9 Csus4 C
goal is to keep me from fall - ing, hey, yeah.

SONG TITLE: HEAVEN

ALBUM: OUR VERSION OF EVENTS

RELEASED: 2011

LABEL: VIRGIN

GENRE: POP

PERSONNEL: EMELI SANDÉ (VOX)

UK CHART PEAK: 2

US CHART PEAK: N/A

BACKGROUND INFO

'Heaven' was the lead single from Emeli Sandé's debut album, *Our Version Of Events*.

THE BIGGER PICTURE

Adele Emeli Sandé was born in Sunderland, England in 1987, but was brought up in Alford, Scotland. Her parents placed a high value on education and Sandé was very studious as a schoolchild. At home, she would indulge her love of music by playing recorder, clarinet and piano. Sandé wrote her first song aged 11 for a school talent contest. She later said: "That was the first time I thought I might be a songwriter." At 15, Sandé won an urban music talent show run by BBC Three. "I won and got to go to London, to see people in record companies," Sandé said, "but I found it overwhelming." The young singer-songwriter went back to Scotland to focus on her studies, but kept writing in her spare time. While studying for a degree in neuroscience at Glasgow University, Sandé wrote a Top 10 hit for Chipmunk entitled 'Diamond Rings'. The success of that song encouraged Sandé to take the plunge by quitting her studies and moving to London. There, she wrote for artists such as Cheryl Cole and Leona Lewis before finally releasing her own record in 2011.

NOTES

'Heaven' was written during the writing sessions for Emeli Sandé's debut album, *Our Version Of Events*. When it was released as a single it stood out for its unusual production, which harks back to the trip hop and drum and bass styles of the 1990s. "A lot of people when they first hear it immediately think early '90s, that kind of era" said Sandé, "Strings with the 'Funky Drummer' [drum sample] underneath them, quite epic sounding I guess. The song was written after a very long conversation I had with [producer and co-writer] Naughty Boy… about religion and how to be good – what we all try to do in this day and age and how difficult it is. He said, 'I guess you just have to keep your heart clean' and that sparked the whole song. It was done really quickly and we knew it was a special one as soon as it was done." Sandé's record company agreed and released it as the lead single from her debut album.

RECOMMENDED LISTENING

Emeli Sandé's debut album, *Our Version Of Events*, was an international chart success that showcased two qualities Sandé strives for in her music: "honesty" and "raw emotion". Stylistically, it's sophisticated pop without much of the urban edge of 'Heaven'.

Heaven

Emeli Sandé

Words & Music by Emeli Sandé, Mike Spencer, Harry Craze,
Shahid Khan & Hugo Chegwin

1. Will you re-cog-nise me in the flash - ing lights?
2. Will you re-cog-nise me when I'm steal - ing from the poor?

Female Vocals Grade 7

20

© Copyright 2011 Stellar Songs Limited/Naughty Words Limited.
EMI Music Publishing Limited/Sony/ATV Music Publishing.
All Rights Reserved. International Copyright Secured.

Les Misérables

SONG TITLE: I DREAMED A DREAM
ALBUM: LES MISÉRABLES
RELEASED: 2012
LABEL: POLYDOR
GENRE: MUSICAL THEATRE

PERSONNEL: ANNE HATHAWAY (VOX)

UK CHART PEAK: 22
US CHART PEAK: 69

BACKGROUND INFO

'I Dreamed A Dream' was a hit single from the *Les Misérables* movie soundtrack album.

THE BIGGER PICTURE

Les Misérables is a 2012 film based on the musical of the same name. The story is based on the novel *Les Misérables* by French poet and novelist Victor Hugo. It tells of a prisoner named Valjean (imprisoned for stealing bread to feed his starving relative), who is released on parole, escapes and is pursued by the policeman Javert. Valjean begins a new life in another town, where he assumes a new identity and becomes a wealthy factory owner and mayor of the town. Single mother Fantine is a worker at his factory, who is dismissed following an argument with a colleague. To continue supporting her daughter, Cosette, Fantine becomes a prostitute. One night she has a fight with a client and is arrested by Javert. Valjean arrives at the scene and orders Javert to release Fantine, who is taken to a hospital. There, by her death bed, Valjean promises to take care of Cosette. However, Javert recognises Valjean and confronts him, so Valjean escapes again, rescues Cosette from her villainous adoptive family and starts over again in Paris. There the story continues amidst the 1832 Paris Uprising.

Valjean struggles to hide his true identity, while Cosette falls in love with one of the revolutionaries, the student Marius.

NOTES

'I Dreamed A Dream' is sung by Fantine in the film version of *Les Misérables*, after she has been sacked and forced into a life of prostitution. Anne Hathaway's vocals were recorded live on the film set, then added to the backing tracks at the editing stage. Hathaway's performance earned her an Oscar for Best Supporting Actress in 2012. The song was originally published in 1980 and has since been covered by dozens of artists. In 2009, it was performed by Scottish singer Susan Boyle as her audition for TV show *Britain's Got Talent*. Her performance went viral on social media, gaining millions of views in a few weeks.

RECOMMENDED LISTENING

Musical theatre is a genre rich in great vocal performances. Classic singers to watch out for include Elaine Page, Sarah Brightman and Liza Minnelli. The style is as popular today as ever. Pop stars Melanie C and Kimberley Walsh have both recorded musical theatre albums (*Stages* and *Centre Stage,* respectively).

I Dreamed A Dream

© Copyright (Music & Lyrics) 1980 Editions Musicales Alain Boublil.
English Lyrics © Copyright 1985 Alain Boublil Music Limited (ASCAP).
All Rights Reserved. International Copyright Secured.

no song un - sung, no wine un - tas - ted.

More movement

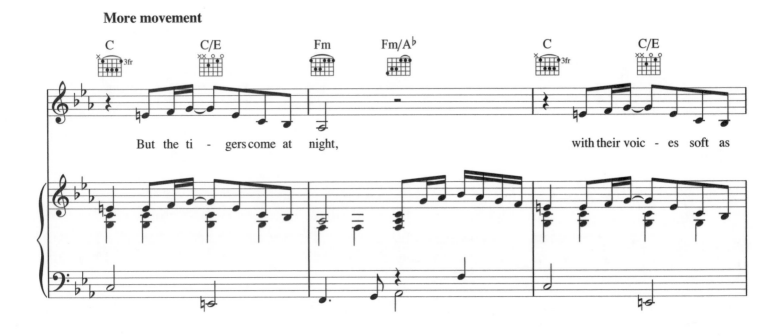

But the ti - gers come at night, with their voic - es soft as

thun - der, as they tear your hopes a -part,

open

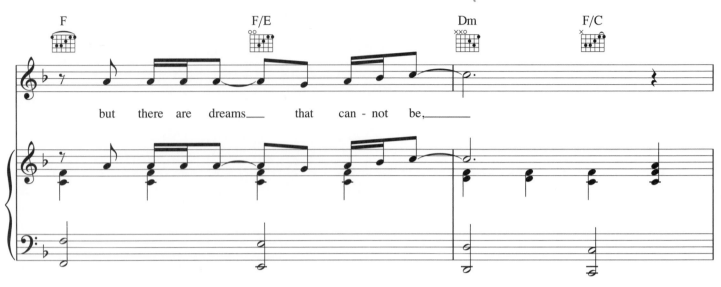

but there are dreams___ that can - not be,_____

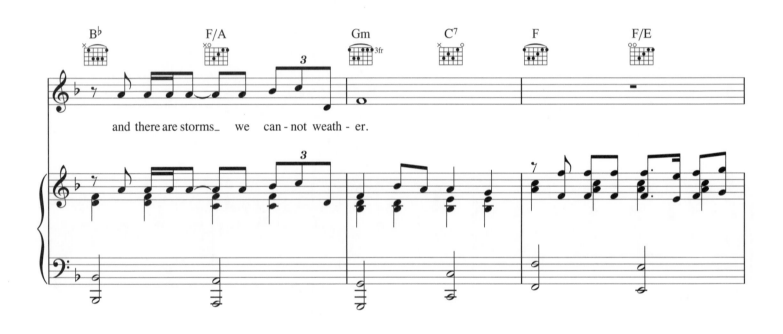

and there are storms_ we can - not weath - er.

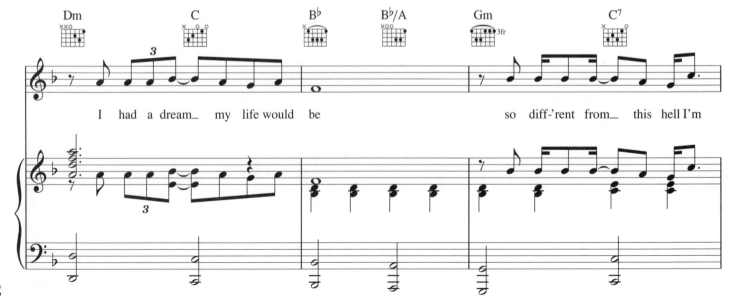

I had a dream_ my life would be   so diff-'rent from_ this hell I'm

liv - ing, so diff -'rent now from what it seemed,

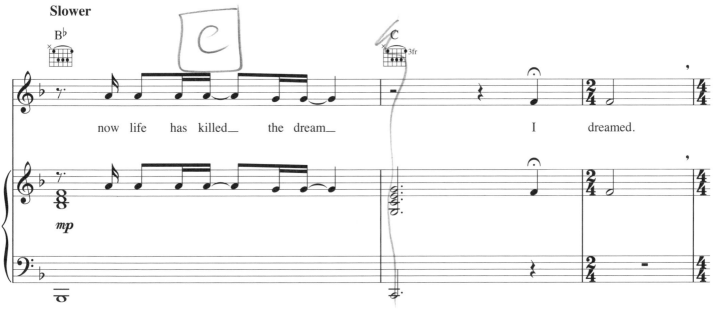

now life has killed___ the dream___ I dreamed.

rit. poco a poco

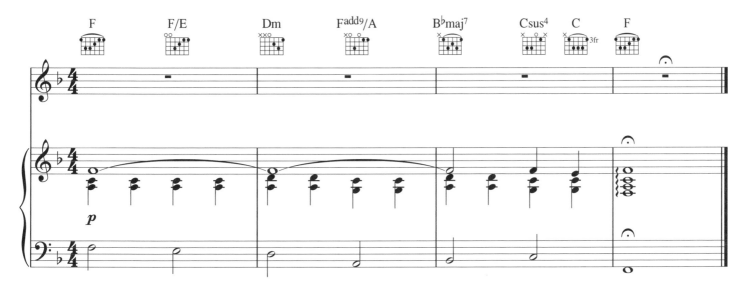

SONG TITLE: AMERICAN BOY
ALBUM: SHINE
RELEASED: 2008
LABEL: ATLANTIC
GENRE: DISCO FUNK

PERSONNEL: ESTELLE (VOX)
KANYE WEST (VOX)
JOHN LEGEND (VOX)
WILL.I.AM (KEYS)
CALEB SPEIR (BASS)

UK CHART PEAK: 1
US CHART PEAK: 9

BACKGROUND INFO

'American Boy' was the second single from English singer/rapper Estelle's studio album *Shine*.

THE BIGGER PICTURE

Estelle Swaray was born in London in 1980. Her father was a session musician and Estelle grew up with an interest in popular music. She and her siblings would get together and perform their favourite pop hits. "If Salt 'n' Pepa were big, we would do that," said Swaray, "If Yazz was big, we would do Yazz." After leaving school, she worked in the record store Deal Real, which was a key player in the UK hip hop scene. Her colleagues in the shop encouraged her to perform as a rapper and she became a regular on London's hip hop scene. A crowd-pleasing performance at the club Subterania brought Estelle to the attention of DJ Skitz, who asked her to perform on his album *Countryman* in 2001. The record was a critical success and helped raise the profile of UK hip hop. Estelle's debut album, *The 18th Day*, was released in 2004 and spawned the Top 40 singles '1980', 'Free' and 'Go Gone'. However, her greatest success came after a chance meeting in Los Angeles with Kanye West, who introduced her to John Legend. The trio worked together on Estelle's second album, *Shine*, and its single 'American Boy'.

NOTES

'American Boy' was written by Estelle, John Legend and Kanye West, based on a sample of will.i.am's song 'Impatient', from his 2007 album *Songs About Girls* (will.i.am also produced 'American Boy'). The song's lyrics came from a suggestion from John Legend: "We were just messing about in the studio, joking around," said Estelle, "and John just said to me, 'Why don't you write a song about meeting an American boy?' So I was like, 'Well, that's pretty easy' – because I have a lot of male friends out there in New York. And I unwittingly ended up creating a new ladies' anthem!" 'American Boy' was a major breakthrough for Estelle, becoming the most successful single of her career.

RECOMMENDED LISTENING

To hear Estelle during her early hip hop period, check out the single '1980' from her debut album, *The 18th Day*. Shine was her breakthrough album, featuring 'American Boy' and the collaboration with John Legend, 'You Are'. Estelle's third album, *All Of Me* (2012), features 'Thank You', an early 1970s soul style track with a lush vocal from Estelle, and 'Do My Thing', featuring Janelle Monáe; while 'Break My Heart', featuring rapper Rick Ross, is a throwback to Estelle's formative days on the hip hop scene.

American Boy

Estelle

Words & Music by Will Adams, John Stephens, Kanye West, Keith Harris,
Josh Lopez, Caleb Speir, Estelle Swaray & Kweli Washington

© Copyright 2008 Will.I.Am Music Inc./John Legend Publishing/Broke Spoke And Gone Publishing/EMI April Music Inc./Songs Of Universal Inc./
Please Gimme My Publishing, Inc./Speir Music/Larry Leron Music/Cue GroupMusic, USA/Chrysalis Music Limited.
BMG Sapphire Songs/EMI Music Publishing Limited/Universal/MCA Music Limited (All rights in Germany administered by Universal/MCA Music Publ. GmbH)/Carlin Music Corporation.
All Rights Reserved. International Copyright Secured.

kick it with you.___ You'll be my A-mer-i-can__ boy.____

1. He said, "Hey sis - ter,_____ it's real-ly real-ly nice to meet__
2. Can we get a-way this week-end?_____ Take__ me__ to Broad-way.____

___ ya." I___ just met__ this five__ foot sev-en guy__ who's just__ my type.__
____ Let's__ go shop-pin', may-be then__ we'll go to a___ caf-é.___

____ Like the way__ he's speak-in', his con-fid-ence__ is peak-
____ Let's go on__ the sub-way, take me to__ your hood,__

SONG TITLE: WHAT'S UP?

ALBUM: BIGGER, BETTER, FASTER, MORE!

RELEASED: 1993

LABEL: INTERSCOPE

GENRE: ROCK

PERSONNEL: LINDA PERRY (VOX+GTR)

LOUIS METOYER (GTR)

CHRISTA HILLHOUSE (BASS)

DAWN RICHARDSON (DRUMS)

UK CHART PEAK: 2

US CHART PEAK: 14

Moderate ♩ = 125

A

BACKGROUND INFO

'What's Up?' was the second single from 4 Non Blondes' studio album, *Bigger, Better, Faster, More!*

THE BIGGER PICTURE

4 Non Blondes formed in San Francisco in 1989. Bassist Christa Hillhouse, guitarist Shauna Hall and drummer Wanda Day had been performing as a trio, but asked Linda Perry to join as lead singer after they saw her perform at a local gig. The four-piece spent the next two years gigging locally, by 1991 earning enough of a reputation to support the band Primus. Following this support slot, the band was signed to Interscope records in summer of the same year. During pre-production on their debut album, Wanda Day was fired because of her drug use and replaced by Dawn Richardson. Day wasn't the only member to go during the recording process, though, as the album's producer David Tickle decided Shauna Hall's guitar playing "wasn't happening". Hall was also fired and Louis Metoyer hired as her temporary replacement (Roger Rocha joined the band on a permanent basis after the album was completed). The album, entitled *Bigger, Better, Faster, More!*, was released in 1992 and became an international hit thanks to the success of single 'What's Going On?' The group split up in 1994.

NOTES

Like most of the songs on 4 Non Blondes' *Bigger, Better, Faster, More!*, 'What's Up?' was written by the group's singer/guitarist Linda Perry. It was called 'What's Up?' rather than the more obvious 'What's Going On?' to avoid confusion with Marvin Gaye's song of the same name. After 4 Non Blondes disbanded, Perry signed a contract as a solo artist with the group's record label, Interscope. However, she failed to achieve the kind of success enjoyed briefly by 4 Non Blondes. Perry later became a successful songwriter, writing for other artists. Her break as a songwriter came when the singer Pink asked her to help write and produce her second album *Missandaztood*. The success of Pink's album led to Perry writing for many of the biggest stars of the early 21st century, including Christina Aguilera ('Beautiful') and Gwen Stefani ('What You Waiting For?').

RECOMMENDED LISTENING

4 Non Blondes' five years together produced only one album, 1992's *Bigger, Better, Faster, More!* (The band had made a start on its follow-up when they split up in 1994). Their only album is a satisfying blend of alternative rock and pop influences that justifies its popularity.

What's Up?

4 Non Blondes

Words & Music by Linda Perry

© Copyright 1993 Stuck In The Throat.
Famous Music Corporation.
All Rights Reserved. International Copyright Secured.

Technical Exercises

Group A: Scales

The harmonic minor scale should be prepared as shown below. You may select any starting note from A–E. You will be asked if you would like to sing along to a metronome click or hear four clicks before you start. Whichever option you choose, you will hear your chosen starting note before the count starts. You may perform this test using any vocal sound except humming or whistling. The tempo is ♩=100.

Group B: Arpeggios

In this group, the arpeggio exercise needs to be prepared as shown below.

This test is performed to a metronome click track and you may select any starting note from C–G. You will hear the root note played on piano followed by a one-bar (three click) count-in. You may perform this test using any vocal sound except humming or whistling. The tempo is ♩=100.

C augmented arpeggio

Group C: Intervals

In this group, both the major and minor interval sequences need to be prepared as below. You will be asked to perform one of them in the exam, as chosen by the examiner.

The examiner will choose a starting note within the range A–C. You will hear this note followed by a four-beat count-in. You may perform this test using any vocal sound except humming or whistling. The tempo is ♩=90.

Major 3rd and major 2nd intervals

Minor 3rd and minor 2nd intervals

Group D: Backing Vocals

In this group, all three backing vocal parts need to be prepared as shown below. You will be asked to perform one of them in the exam, as chosen by the examiner. The chosen part must be sung alongside the other two parts on the recording. The backing tracks for these can be found on the download card.

Group E: Stylistic Studies

You will need to choose *one* stylistic technical study from the group of styles listed below. Your choice will determine the style of the Quick Study Piece. If you choose the jazz and blues stylistic study, for example, the examiner will give you a QSP from the jazz and blues group.

- Pop and musical theatre
- Soul and R'n'B
- Jazz and blues
- Rock and indie

Stylistic Study | Pop and Musical Theatre   *Controlling dynamic legato and staccato phrasing / Wide pitch jumps*

Stylistic Study | Soul and R'n'B   *Trill downs / Onset note bends to sustain*

Stylistic Study | Jazz and Blues

Edge/fry on scoops and onsets / Chromatic step phrasing

Stylistic Study | Rock and Indie

Dramatic dynamics / Sustain note bends

Quick Study Piece

At this grade you will be asked to prepare and perform a short Quick Study Piece (QSP). This will consist of four bars of melody and eight bars of improvisation. Bars 1–4 of the test will be a notated melody and you will need to sing all the written detail including lyrics. In bars 5–8, you will need to improvise a variation on bars 1–4, developing both the lyrics and melody as you feel appropriate. In bars 9–12, you will need to improvise with no requirement to reference bars 1–4. You may use any vocal sound except humming or whistling for these bars.

The examiner will give you the sheet music, then you will hear a full mix version of the track, including the notated parts. This first playthrough will be preceded by the root note and a one-bar count-in. After the full mix, you will have three minutes to practise. The root note will be played at the start of this practice time and then again after 90 seconds. During the practice time, you will be given the choice of a metronome click throughout or a one-bar count-in at the beginning.

At the end of three minutes, the backing track will be played twice more with the notated parts now absent. The first time is for you to rehearse and the second time is for you to perform the final version for the exam. Again, you will hear the root note and a one-bar count-in before both playthroughs. The backing track is continuous, so once the first playthrough has finished, the root note and count-in of the second playthrough will start immediately. The tempo is ♩=70–160.

The QSP style will be from one of the following four groups. These match the groups of the stylistic studies in the Technical Exercises section.

- Pop and musical theatre
- Soul and R'n'B
- Jazz and blues
- Rock and indie

The style given to you in the exam will be from the same group as your choice of stylistic study. The examiner will decide which one, specifically (i.e. rock *or* indie).

Quick Study Piece | Pop and Musical Theatre *Example test*

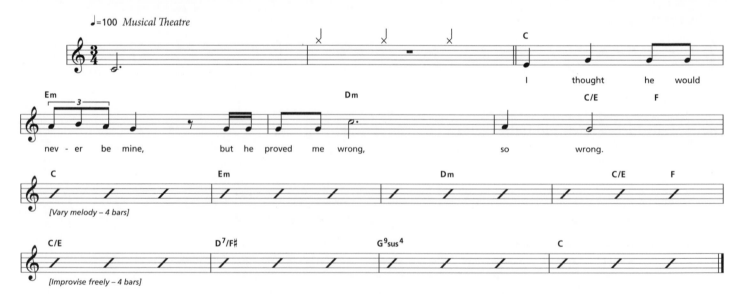

Quick Study Piece | Soul and R'n'B

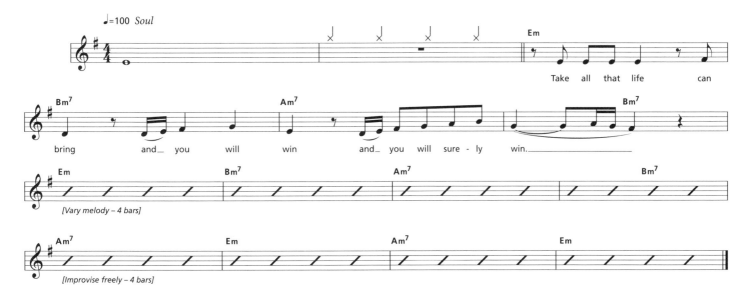

Take all that life can
bring and you will win and you will sure-ly win.

[Vary melody – 4 bars]

[Improvise freely – 4 bars]

Quick Study Piece | Jazz and Blues

Last train is leav-ing, rol - ling out the sta-tion. Gone down the tracks and take___ my dreams a - way.

[Vary melody – 4 bars]

[Improvise freely – 4 bars]

Quick Study Piece | Rock and Indie

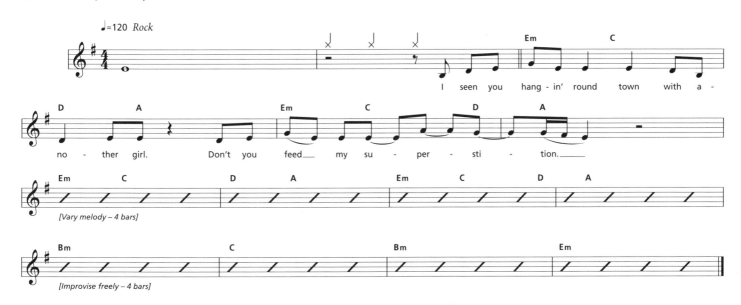

I seen you hang-in' round town with a - no - ther girl. Don't you feed___ my su - per-sti - tion.___

[Vary melody – 4 bars]

[Improvise freely – 4 bars]

Ear Tests

In this section, there are two ear tests:

- Melodic Recall
- Harmony Vocals

You will find one example of each type of test printed below and you will be given both of them in the exam.

Test 1 | Melodic Recall

The examiner will play you a two-bar melody played to a drum backing. It will use the B major or D natural minor scales (the examiner will decide which) and the first note will be the root note or the 5th. You will hear the test twice. Each time the test is played, it starts with the root note and a four-beat count-in. There will be a short gap for you to practise after each playthrough. Next, you will hear a *vocal* count-in, after which you should sing the melody to the drum backing. The tempo is ♩=90.

It is acceptable to sing over the track as it is being played as well as practising after the first two playthroughs. The length of time available after the second playthrough is pre-recorded on the audio track, so the vocal count-in may begin while you are still practising.

You may perform this test using any vocal sound except humming or whistling.

Please note: the test shown is an example. The examiner will give you a different version in the exam.

Test 2 | Harmony Vocals

The examiner will play you a four-bar melody in the key of either A major or E minor, based on any diatonic chords. The recorded vocal part will sing the root, 3rd or 5th of each chord, and you will need to harmonise a diatonic 3rd or 4th above this part using the same rhythm. The examiner will give you the lyrics.

You will hear the test twice. Each time the test is played, it starts with the root note and a four-beat count-in. There will be a short gap for you to practise after each playthrough. Next, you will hear a *vocal* count-in, after which you should perform the harmony line. The tempo is ♩=90–130.

It is acceptable to sing over the track as it is being played as well as practising after the first two playthroughs. The length of time available after the second playthrough is pre-recorded on the audio track, so the vocal count-in may begin while you are still practising.

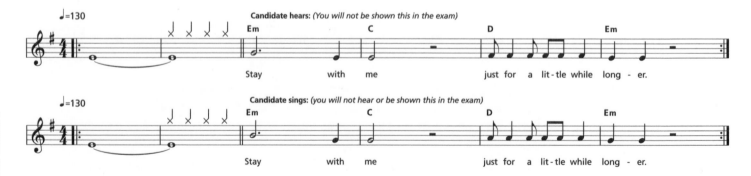

Please note: the test shown is an example. The examiner will give you a different version in the exam.

General Musicianship Questions

In this part of the exam you will be asked five questions. Three of these will be about general music knowledge, the fourth will be about improvisation and the fifth will be about your voice or the microphone.

Part 1 | General Music Knowledge

The examiner will ask three music knowledge questions from the categories below. The questions will be based on one of the pieces (including Free Choice Pieces) as performed by you in the exam. You can choose which one.

If there are handwritten notes on the piece you have chosen, the examiner may ask you to choose an alternative.

You will be asked to *identify and explain:*
- Any notation used in the chosen piece.
- Recognition of intervals up to an octave between two adjacent notes. (You will need to state major, minor or perfect).

Part 2 | Improvisation

You will be asked to briefly *describe and demonstrate* – with reference to melody, rhythm, phrasing, dynamics and expression – your approach to how you would improvise any part of your chosen song. You can choose the part.

Part 3 | Your Voice And The Microphone

The examiner will also ask you one question about your voice or the microphone. Brief demonstrations to assist your answer would be acceptable.

You will be asked:
- What type of exercise might you use to practise 'flipping between registers', including the pitches you would use in the exercise for your voice?
- Give two examples of vocal effects you might employ while singing in the rock style.
- Explain the difference between 'warm-ups' and 'technical practice', including one example of the type of exercise used for each.
- What equalization settings might you use to correct a singer with a very 'nasal' sound?

Entering Exams, Exam Procedure & Marking Schemes

Entering Exams

Entering a Rockschool exam is easy. You can enter online at *www.rockschool.co.uk* or by downloading and filling in an exam entry form. The full Rockschool examination terms and conditions as well as exam periods and current fees are available from our website or by calling +44 (0)845 460 4747.

Exam procedure

In the exam you can decide whether to start with the Performance Pieces or the Technical Exercises. These will be followed by the Supporting Tests (Ear Tests and Quick Study Pieces) and General Musicianship Questions.

Use Of Microphone

At Level 1 (Grades 1–3) microphone use is optional, although candidates may use one if they feel it will enhance their performance. At Level 2 (Grades 4–5) microphone use is obligatory for all pieces and at Level 3 (Grades 6–8) for the whole exam.

Marking Schemes

Below are the marking schemes for the two different types of Rockschool exam.

GRADE EXAMS | GRADES 6–8

ELEMENT	PASS	MERIT	DISTINCTION
Performance Piece 1	12–14 out of 20	15–17 out of 20	18+ out of 20
Performance Piece 2	12–14 out of 20	15–17 out of 20	18+ out of 20
Performance Piece 3	12–14 out of 20	15–17 out of 20	18+ out of 20
Technical Exercises	9–10 out of 15	11–12 out of 15	13+ out of 15
Quick Study Piece	6 out of 10	7–8 out of 10	9+ out of 10
Ear Tests	6 out of 10	7–8 out of 10	9+ out of 10
General Musicianship Questions	3 out of 5	4 out of 5	5 out of 5
TOTAL MARKS	60%+	74%+	90%+

PERFORMANCE CERTIFICATES | GRADES 1–8

ELEMENT	PASS	MERIT	DISTINCTION
Performance Piece 1	12–14 out of 20	15–17 out of 20	18+ out of 20
Performance Piece 2	12–14 out of 20	15–17 out of 20	18+ out of 20
Performance Piece 3	12–14 out of 20	15–17 out of 20	18+ out of 20
Performance Piece 4	12–14 out of 20	15–17 out of 20	18+ out of 20
Performance Piece 5	12–14 out of 20	15–17 out of 20	18+ out of 20
TOTAL MARKS	60%+	75%+	90%+

Improvisation Requirements & Free Choice Pieces

At Rockschool it is our aim to encourage creativity and individualism. We therefore give candidates the opportunity to express themselves musically within styles of their own choice. For this reason, Free Choice Pieces are accepted in all Vocals grades. In addition, all songs performed in exams from Grade 3 onwards have compulsory improvisation requirements.

Improvisation Requirements

From Grade 3, all songs, whether from the grade book or chosen as FCPs, need to incorporate improvisation. The improvisation can be prepared in advance, but is expected to be individually constructed, and needs to include **both** vocal ad-libbing and re-working of existing melody lines as follows:

Level 1 Grade 3:   Vocal ad-libbing (2–4 bars) and re-working of melody line (4 bars)
Level 2 Grades 4–5:   Vocal ad-libbing (4–8 bars) and re-working of melody line (4–8 bars)
Level 3 Grades 6–7:   Vocal ad-libbing (8–12 bars) and re-working of melody line (8 bars)
Level 3 Grades 8:   Vocal ad-libbing (12–16 bars) and re-working of melody line (8 bars)

For all pieces, you will need to highlight the sheet music to show the examiner the location of both ad-libbed and re-worked parts at the beginning of the exam.

Notes

- You are free to choose where you improvise. However, in all cases, improvisations need to be a continuous number of bars, not a number of smaller bars which in total add up to the ranges shown.

- Vocal ad-lib could be demonstrated in, for example, introductions, endings or open instrumental parts.

- Re-working of a melody could be demonstrated by altering any existing singing parts; for example, verses, choruses, bridges.

- For both ad-lib and re-working of a melody, you need to demonstrate an awareness of harmony, melody, phrasing, use of rhythms and incorporation of any appropriate expression in a stylistically appropriate manner. Range and content will be expected to increase progressively as you move through the grades.

- We would encourage re-working to take place later in a piece after the original has been presented to show you can portray the original, then you are able to adapt appropriately with individual colour.

- Improvisation can be a good place to demonstrate your head voice, which can often be omitted, reducing the technical content of a piece at a particular grade.

Free Choice Pieces (FCPs)

An FCP is defined as any piece outside the grade book, and can fall into two categories:

1) **Wider Repertoire:** a full list of pre-approved and regularly updated pieces can be found on *www.rockschool.co.uk*. These songs can be used **without** prior approval from Rockschool.

2) **Own Choice:** candidates can choose any song in any genre outside the grade book and wider repertoire. These songs can, however, only be used **with** prior approval from Rockschool. This requirement is compulsory and you need to contact the office to have your chosen piece(s) approved. Please allow five weeks before your exam to receive a decision.

We cannot accept any songs which have not been approved or are not contained in the grade book or wider repertoire.

For all grades, candidates can choose the following number of FCPs in the exam:
Grade Examinations: Up to 2 of 3 pieces can be free choice. (At least one piece must be from the grade book.)
Performance Certificates: Up to 3 of 5 pieces can be free choice. (At least two pieces must be from the grade book.)

For all FCPs, candidates will need to bring the sheet music and a backing track (without vocal part) on the day. A memory stick, iPod or CD/DVD is acceptable and we would also suggest a second source to be safe. It will not be necessary to bring the sheet music or backing tracks for pieces chosen from the grade book.

Copyright Information

Big Spender
(Fields/Coleman)
Campbell Connelly & Company Limited

Bleeding Love
(McCartney/Tedder)
Warner/Chappell Artemis Music Limited/Kobalt Music Publishing Limited

Heaven
(Sandé/Spencer/Craze/Khan/Chegwin)
EMI Music Publishing Limited/ Sony/ATV Music Publishing (UK) Limited

I Dreamed A Dream (from 'Les Miserables')
(Schönberg/Boublil/Natel/Kretzmer)
Warner/Chappell North America Limited

American Boy
Adams/Stephens/West/Harris/Lopez/Speir/Swaray/Washington)
Universal/MCA Music Limited/BMG Rights Management (UK) Limited/EMI Music Publishing Limited/
Chrysalis Music Limited/Wixen Music UK Ltd

What's Up
(Perry)
Sony/ATV Harmony UK

mcps